Disney's
Family Storybook Library

There's Always
Something to Celebrate

Stories About Happiness

BOOK TWELVE

There's Always Something to Celebrate

Stories About Happiness

Introduction

Children have an inherent exuberance and sense of
joy. For them, the world is just unfolding, and they're
usually delighted with what comes their way. There is,
truly, always something to celebrate—whether it's the
arrival of spring, a new baby, an improved grade, or
a family outing. Encourage your children's enthusiasm
and love of life; it will stand them in good stead in the
years to come.

Cinderella, who asks for so little, receives a generous
surprise at the hands of her animal friends. Alice learns
a valuable lesson about the importance of celebrating the
milestones in our lives. Both Cinderella and Alice are
gracious—happy in giving as well as receiving.

Cinderella's Surprise

from *Cinderella*

Doing a good deed is a gift you can give yourself.

Every morning, the rays of the sun shone into Cinderella's room. Little birds flew in her window, chirping for her to wake up.

"Good morning!" Cinderella sang to them.

The birds flew around the shabby room, helping Cinderella get dressed. They didn't care that her dress was patched and old. They loved her because she was always so cheerful and kind.

Cinderella loved her feathered friends, too. Her stepmother and stepsisters treated her so

poorly that the only joy she had was the
happy birds' singing. That and her dreams.

There was no time for dreaming this
morning, though. The birds had an important
message for Cinderella.

"What?" Cinderella asked, trying to

understand them. "A mouse is caught in a trap? Oh, the poor thing!"

Cinderella ran down the stairs. A mouse was trembling in the back of the rat trap.

Gently, Cinderella set the mouse free. "I'll call you Gus," she decided.

Gus quickly realized that
Cinderella was his friend.
She gave him his
own little sweater
and cap and all
the corn he
could carry.

"Now,
Jacques,
take care
of Gus,"
she told
a skinny
mouse. "And
don't forget to
warn him about
the cat!"

Cinderella hummed as she

did her daily chores. In her mind, she was far away, dancing with her true love. A knock on the door brought her out of her daydreams. "A message from the King!" announced the courier. Cinderella quickly brought the message to her stepmother. "There's to be a ball!" exclaimed the stepmother. "And every young maiden in the land is invited! Of course, you will need to wear something suitable."

The stepsisters squealed. Before long, Cinderella found herself busy sewing and ironing beautiful ball gowns for them. There was no time to make a dress for herself.

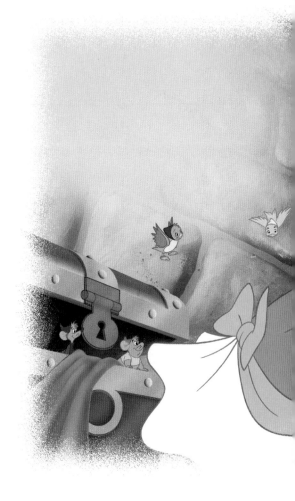

"Poor Cinderelly." Jacques sighed. "She never gets to have any fun."

"She's always helped us. Now we can help her!" chirped the birds suddenly. "We'll make a dress for her so she can go, too!"

The animals scurried about with bits of ribbon and lace and thread. That evening, a very tired and sad Cinderella opened the door to her tiny room.

"Surprise!" shouted the animals. There was the most beautiful ball gown awaiting her. Cinderella's face lit up. Her friends were delighted. They had helped make their favorite person's dream come true.

A Silly Celebration

from *Alice in Wonderland*

⟨⟨⟨⟨

You can always find something to celebrate.

While looking for the March Hare, Alice came upon him and the Mad Hatter as well, drinking tea at a long beautifully decorated table, surrounded by

a picket fence. She sat down at their table and they offered her some tea. She accepted happily, trying to ignore the fact that they were spilling more tea than they were pouring.

"I'm sorry I interrupted your birthday party," she said politely.

"Birthday?" the March Hare snorted. "My dear child, this is not a birthday party!

"This is an *un*birthday party!" the Mad Hatter chimed in. When Alice just looked at him blankly, he went on to explain why unbirthdays were so much better than birthdays. With everyone getting just one birthday each year, the March Hare pointed out, that left 364 unbirthdays to celebrate. And that is just what the Mad Hatter and the March Hare were doing.

Alice considered the idea for a moment,
then laughed out loud. "Why, then today

is my unbirthday, too!" she announced
happily.

"It is?" the Mad Hatter said. "What a small world!" Tipping his hat in honor of Alice, he removed from under it a lovely unbirthday cake, which he presented to her with a flourish.

While Alice admired her cake, the Mad Hatter and the March Hare joined hands and danced around her, singing a very merry unbirthday song.

"Now blow out the candle, my dear," said the Mad Hatter.

Alice made a wish, and then blew as hard as she

could. *Whoosh!* For a moment the golden flame on the candle sizzled and fizzled. Then, like a rocket, the cake blasted off and zoomed high into the sky. Alice gasped as a dazzling explosion of fireworks rained down all around her.

It was all so strange and wonderful. Alice loved every minute of the unbirthday party. And to think—she had 363 more unbirthdays to celebrate that year!